Bibbilibo[...]

more rhymes to

ARNOLD-WHEATON

Bibbilibonty

On the Bibbilibonty hill
Stands a Bibbilibonty house;
In the Bibbilibonty house
Are Bibbilibonty people;
The Bibbilibonty people
Have Bibbilibonty children;
And the Bibbilibonty children
Take a Bibbilibonty sup
With a Bibbilibonty spoon
From a Bibbilibonty cup.

Slap Bang

Slap Bang,
   the dirty man,
Washed his face
   in the frying pan,
And after that,
   he skinned the cat,
And made it into
   a hairy hat.

If I had a donkey

If I had a donkey
And he wouldn't go,
Do you think I'd wallop him?
Oh, no no.
I'd put him in the barn,
And give him some corn,
The best little donkey
That ever was born.

Had a mule

Had a mule,
 his name was Jack;
I rode his tail
 to save his back;
His tail got loose
 and I fell back.
Whoa, Jack!

Misty-moisty

Misty-moisty was the morn,
And cloudy was the weather.
There I met an old man,
Dressed all in leather.
Dressed all in leather,
Against the wind and rain.
With a how do you do?
And a how do you do?
And a how do you do, again.

Policeman, policeman

Policeman, policeman,
  don't catch me!
Catch that boy
  behind that tree.
He stole apples,
  I stole none;
Put him in the jailhouse,
  just for fun.

Oh, Aunt Jenny

Oh, Aunt Jenny,
Look at Uncle Jim!
He fell in the duck pond,
And he's learning
how to swim.

Oh dear!

Auntie Lucy
Sat on a goosey.
Whoop — said the goosey ....
Away flew Aunt Lucy.

Mary lost her coat

Mary lost her coat,
Mary lost her hat,
Mary lost her fifty cents —
Now what do you think of that?

Mary found her coat,
Mary found her hat,
Mary found her fifty cents —
Now what do you think of that?

Me and my granny

Me and my granny
And the old grey mare
Kicked up a row
Going home from the fair.
By came a policeman,
And said, "Who's there?"
"Just me and my granny
And the old grey mare."

What's in there?

What's in there?
  Gold and money.
Where's my share?
  The mousie's run away with it.
Where's the mousie?
  In her housie.
Where's her housie?
  In the wood.
Where's the wood?
  The fire burnt it.
Where's the fire?
  The water quenched it.

Where's the water?
 The brown bull drank it.
Where's the brown bull?
 Behind Burnie's Hill.
Where's Burnie's Hill?
 All covered in snow.
Where's the snow?
 The sun melted it.
Where's the sun?
 High, high, up in the sky.

Two skipping rhymes

Granny, Granny, I am ill;
Send for the doctor to give me a pill.
Doctor, Doctor, shall I die?
Yes you must and so must I.
How many carriages shall I have?
Ten, twenty, thirty, forty, fifty, sixty,
    seventy, eighty, ninety, a HUNDRED!

Acka-backa soda cracker,
Does your father chew tobacco?
Yes, no, maybe so,
Yes, no, maybe so . . . . .

The fox

The fox jumped up
one moon-lit night,
The stars were shining
and all things bright.
"Oh-ho," said the fox,
"It's a very fine night
For me to go through
the town–O."

At last he came
to the farmer's gate,
And what did he see
but the farmer's drake.
"Oh-ho," said the fox,
"What a dinner you will make!
And I'll soon be picking
your bones–O!"

He put a grey goose
on his back,
And took the big duck
by the neck.
The duck, it cried out,
"Quack, quack, quack!"
Its legs all dangling
down–O.

Then old Mrs Slipper Slopper
    jumped out of bed,
And out of the window
    she popped her head,
Crying, "John! John!
    The grey goose is gone!
And the fox is off
    to his den–O!"

Then John went up
    to the top of the hill,
And blew his horn
    both loud and shrill.
Said the fox,
    "That is fine music! Still,
I'd rather be off
    to my den–O!"

So the fox, he trotted
off to his den,
To his dear little foxes,
eight, nine, ten.
He said, "We're in luck!
Here's a big fat duck,
And a goose dangling down
behind–O."

The fox sat down
with his hungry wife.
They ate up their dinner,
without fork or knife.
He said it was the best
he had eaten in his life,
And the little ones picked
the bones–O.

Miss Mary Mac

Miss Mary Mac, Mac, Mac,
All dressed in black, black, black,
With silver buttons, buttons, buttons,
All down her back, back, back.
She asked her mother, mother, mother,
For fifteen cents, cents, cents,
To see the elephant, elephant, elephant,
Jump the fence, fence, fence.

He jumped so high, high, high,
He reached the sky, sky, sky,
And didn't come back, back, back,
Till the fourth of July, ly, ly.
    July can walk, walk, walk;
    July can talk, talk, talk;
    July can eat, eat, eat,
    With a knife and fork, fork, fork.

My mother said

My mother said
  that I never should
Play with the gipsies
  in the wood.
The wood was dark,
The grass was green,
In came Sally
  with a tambourine.

I went to the river,
No ship to get across,
I paid five pounds
   for an old grey horse.
I jumped on his back,
And was off in a crack;
Sally, tell your mother
   I will never come back.

The Key of the Kingdom

This is the key of the kingdom.
In that kingdom is a city;
In that city is a town;
In that town there is a street;
In that street there is a lane;
In that lane there is a yard;
In that yard there is a house;
In that house there is a room;
In that room, an empty bed,
And on that bed, a basket—
A basket of sweet flowers,
    Of flowers, of flowers,
A basket of sweet flowers.

Flowers in the basket,
Basket on the bed,
Bed in the room,
Room in the house,
House in the weedy yard,
Yard in the winding lane,
Lane in the broad street,
Street in the high town,
Town in the city,
City in the kingdom,
This is the key of the kingdom.
Of the kingdom, this is the key.

25

Peter went fishing
on
Sunday

Peter went fishing on Sunday, threw
in his line and caught a large fish, which,
when caught, opened his mouth and sang:
"Take me home, Peter, Peter, Peter!
Oh, mah, ding!"
Peter took him home.

"Kill me now, Peter, Peter, Peter!
Oh, mah, ding!"
And so Peter killed him.
"Clean me now, Peter, Peter, Peter!
Oh, mah, ding!"
And so Peter cleaned him.
"Salt me now, Peter, Peter, Peter!
Oh, mah, ding!"
And so Peter salted him.
"Cook me now, Peter, Peter, Peter!
Oh, mah, ding!"
And so Peter cooked him.
"Eat me now, Peter, Peter, Peter!
Oh, mah, ding!"
And so Peter ate him.
"I got you now, Peter, Peter, Peter!
Oh, mah, ding!"

And Peter never was seen any more!

Betty Botter

(Can you read this very fast?)

Betty Botter bought some butter,
But she said, "This butter's bitter.
If I put it in my batter,
It will make my batter bitter.
But a bit of better butter
Would make my batter better."
So she bought a bit of butter,
Better than her bitter butter,
And she put it in her batter,
And it made her batter better.
So 'twas better Betty Botter
Bought a bit of better butter.

The firefly

I went down a narrow, narrow road,
and I lost my cap.
   The firefly found it.
  "Firefly, firefly, give me back my
     cap!"
  "I won't give you your cap unless
     you give me some bread."

I went to the lady of the house.
  "Lady, give me some bread!"
  "I won't give you bread unless
     you give me some milk."

I went to the cow.
  "Oh, cow, give me some milk!"
  "I won't give you milk unless you
      give me some hay."

I went to the meadow.
  "Oh, meadow, give me hay!"
  "I won't give you hay unless you
      give me a scythe."

I went to the blacksmith.
  "Oh, blacksmith, give me a scythe!"
  "I won't give you a scythe unless
      you give me some lard."

I went to the pig.
  "Oh, pig, give me lard!"
  "I won't give you lard, unless you
      give me acorns."

I went to the oak.
  "Oh, oak, give me acorns!"
  "I won't give you acorns unless
      you bring me the wind."

I went to the sea and I brought
back the wind.
Then I picked up my acorns;
I took the acorns to the pig.
The pig gave me lard;
I took the lard to the blacksmith.
The blacksmith gave me a scythe;
I took the scythe to the meadow.
The meadow gave me hay;
I took the hay to the cow.
The cow gave me milk;
I took the milk to the lady.
The lady gave me bread;
I took the bread to the firefly,
And he gave me back my cap.